LITTLE RED
RIDING

Longman

A woodcutter worked in a forest. He and his
family lived in a small house beside the forest.

One morning the woodcutter's wife put some things into a basket. Her daughter watched her. People called the little girl "Little Red Riding Hood" because she had a red coat with a hood.

4

Her mother said, "I've put some nice cakes and some bread in this basket. Please take it to your grandmother. She isn't very well. Go through the forest, but stay on the path. Give the cakes and bread to your grandmother, and then hurry back."

"Yes, mother," said Little Red Riding Hood.

She started along the path through the forest.
The birds and the small animals followed her.
They weren't afraid of her.

She saw some pretty flowers near the path,
and she thought, "Grandmother will like these."
She picked some. Then she saw some prettier
flowers among the forest trees. She forgot her
mother's words: "stay on the path." When all
the little animals ran away, she didn't know.

Suddenly there was a noise behind her. She looked up, and she heard: "Good morning, little girl."

It was the Big Bad Wolf. But Little Red Riding Hood didn't know that. She answered: "Good morning, sir."

"Tell me, my dear," said the wolf. "Where are you going this fine day?"

"I'm going to see my grandmother. She lives in the forest," said Red Riding Hood. "But I'm afraid I'm not on the path."

"Hmm! And what do you have in your basket?" the wolf asked.

"Oh, some nice things for grandmother. She isn't well."

"Does your grandmother live alone?" the wolf asked.

"Yes, she lives alone," said the little girl.

10

The wolf looked at the basket, and his mouth watered because he was very hungry. But he thought, "I must wait. Then I'll get a better meal." So he said, "Now, let me take you back to the path. Then you'll be all right."

"Thank you," Red Riding Hood said, and she followed him to the path.

"Does your grandmother live far from here?" the wolf asked.

"Not very far," she said. "In the little house beside the path. I can go in easily because she doesn't lock the door."

"Oh, really! Really!" said the wolf, and his mouth watered again. "Now stay on the path. And I hope your grandmother tastes – er – *feels* better soon."

"Thank you," said Little Red Riding Hood. She waved goodbye and went along the path.

The Big Bad Wolf ran very quickly through the forest. He arrived at the house before Red Riding Hood. He looked through the window. Yes, the old woman was really alone. He knocked on the door.

"Who's there?" the old woman called.

"Me, Little Red Riding Hood, with some food from mother," said the wolf in a high voice.

"Come in, dear. The door isn't locked."

The wolf opened the door and jumped at the old woman. She was so afraid that she fainted. The wolf wanted to eat her at once, but he heard Red Riding Hood outside. He quickly pushed the old woman into a cupboard. Then he put her nightclothes on, and jumped into the bed.

Red Riding Hood knocked on the door.

"Who's there?" called the wolf in the old woman's voice.

"Me, Little Red Riding Hood, with some food from mother," said the little girl.

"Come in, dear. The door isn't locked," said the wolf.

Red Riding Hood opened the door and looked in. It wasn't very light in the room, but she saw the old woman's nightcap on the pillow.

"I hope you are better," said Little Red Riding Hood.

The wolf didn't answer, but she saw his eyes.

"Oh! What big eyes you've got!" said Red Riding Hood.

"All the better to see you with," the wolf said.

Then Red Riding Hood saw the shape of her grandmother's nightcap, and she said:

"What big ears you've got, grandmother!"

"All the better to hear you with," said the wolf.

She saw the wolf's mouth, and she cried:

"Oh! What big *teeth* you've got, grandmother!"

"Ha! All the better to *eat* you with!"

But suddenly the door opened, and the woodcutter was there with his axe.

The wolf looked angrily at the woodcutter, but he was afraid of the great axe. He jumped through the window, and ran.

Little Red Riding Hood cried, she was so
afraid. Her father put down his axe and held her.

Then they heard a noise from the cupboard.
The woodcutter opened it. Poor grandmother
was there.

They put her into her bed, and she ate some of the cakes. Soon she was much better.

So Little Red Riding Hood and her father went home.

After that, she always stayed on the path. And she only spoke to people she knew.

Pearson Education Limited,
Edinburgh Gate, Harlow,
Essex CM20 2JE, England
and Associated Companies throughout the world.

First published 1989 by Longman Group UK Limited
in association with Bill Melendez Productions Limited
Eighth impression Penguin Books 1999

Set in 14/16 pt Monophoto Univers Medium
Printed in China
EPC/08

ISBN 0-582-02570-2

Adapted by Stan Hayward from the fairy tale by the Charles Perrault;
English Language Teaching Version by D. K. Swan

Illustrations from the animated film *Little Red Riding Hood*
A Bill Melendez Production
Designed by John Challis
Directed by Dick Horn